To my grandson, Julian, who loves
words and wants to know the
meaning of new ones as though they
were new friends.

Published by Concordia Publishing House
3558 S. Jefferson Avenue, St. Louis, MO 63118-3968
Manufactured in the United States of America

1 2 3 4 5 6 7 8 9 10   05 04 03 02 01 00 99 98 97 96

This is the Baby

Eldon Weisheit
Illustrated by Rick Incrocci

SAINT LOUIS

This is the baby,
Born in a stall,
Sent by God to save us all.

This is the mother young and amazed
Who gave birth to the baby,
Born in a stall,
Sent by God to save us all.

These are the animals who shared their home
With the mother young and amazed
Who gave birth to the baby,
Born in a stall,
Sent by God to save us all.

These are the shepherds who searched the town
To find the place the animals shared
With the mother young and amazed.

Who gave birth to the baby,
Born in a stall,
Sent by God to save us all.

These are the angels who sang the songs
That guided the shepherds
Who searched the town
To find the place the animals shared

With the mother young and amazed
Who gave birth to the baby,
Born in a stall,
Sent by God to save us all.

This is the star high in the sky
With the angels who sang the songs
That guided the shepherds
Who searched the town

To find the place the animals shared
With the mother young and amazed
Who gave birth to the baby,
Born in a stall,
Sent by God to save us all.

These are the Wise Men who came from the East
Led by the star high in the sky
With the angels who sang the songs
That guided the shepherds who searched the town.

For the place the animals shared
With the mother young and amazed
Who gave birth to the baby,
Born in a stall,
Sent by God to save us all.

These are the people from all over the world
Who followed the Wise Men who came from the East
Led by the star high in the sky
With the angels who sang the songs.

That guided the shepherds
Who searched the town
For the place the animals shared
With the mother young and amazed

Who gave birth to the baby,
Born in a stall,
Sent by God to save us all.